THE
ULTIMATE
WORKBOOK
FOR CHILDREN

1

www.pegasusforkids.com

Published by Kuldeep Jain for B. Jain Publishers (P) Ltd., D-157, Sector 63, Noida - 201307, U.P.

Registered office: 1921/10, Chuna Mandi, Paharganj, New Delhi-110055

Printed in India

PREFACE

The Ultimate Workbook for Children is a series of eight books — three Pre-Primary workbooks and five Primary workbooks, specially researched and developed for preschoolers on the principle of learning by doing. With a hands-on approach as per the international standards, **The Ultimate Workbook for Children** is an interactive, activity-based series comprising of topics chosen as per children's learning aptitude and interest as well as relevance in day-to-day life.

The series aims at the development of a multi-skilled foundation of learning with focus on-

- **cognitive skills** to observe surroundings and situations and act as per them
- **psychomotor skills** to process information and act accordingly
- **visual** and **linguistic skills** to perceive, sort, compare, and match different colours, shapes, sizes, numbers, letters, and images
- **logical** and **mathematical** reasoning to count, add, and subtract numbers
- **expressing oneself** to develop the ability to recognise and express emotions, empathise with others, learn everyday values.

The Ultimate Workbook for Children series is well-curated with creative illustrations and designs along with level-appropriate content for the young children. The classroom-based course books explain concepts in a fun and interactive way in the form of easy-to-understand text, illustrations, poems, and activities. The well-researched workbooks provide ample scope for children to brainstorm and revise the concepts at home independently or with the support of elders.

The Ultimate Workbook for Children series helps mould the young learners to become active participants in the society at a globally-developed level. Children learn new things everyday by exploring their surroundings. **The Ultimate Workbook for Children** series instigates children to learn concepts and apply them in their daily routines for their over-all growth.

Contents

Words 5

Phonics 37

Vocabulary 71

Maths 87

My World 105

Science.. 121

Thinking Skills 139

Life Skills.................................... 151

Fun With Colours 165

Activities.................................... 181

WORDS

A B C D

The names of these animals all start with the letters a, b, c and d.
Match the letters with the pictures.

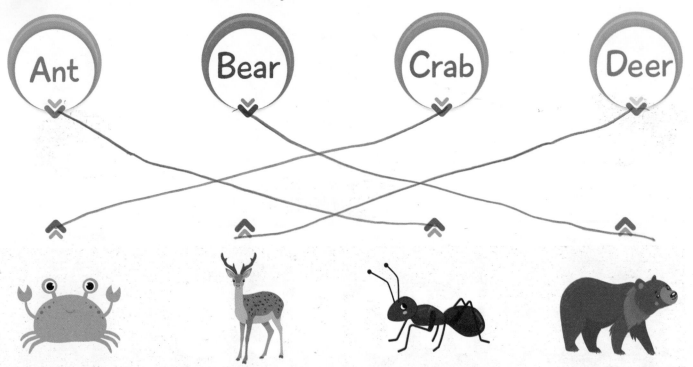

Colour the pictures given below by following the colour code.
Write the first letter of the picture in the blanks.

A. ●   B. ●   C. ●   D. ●

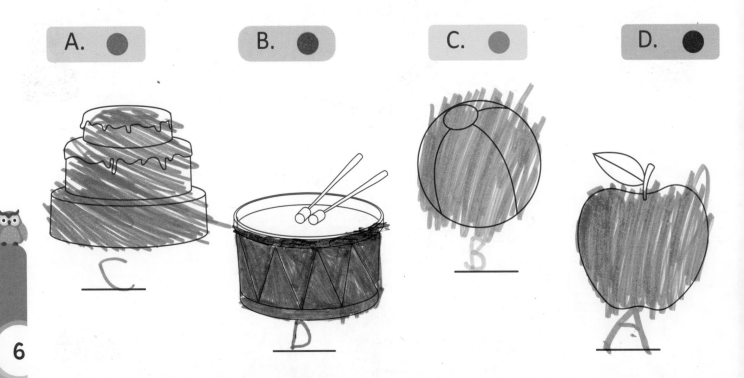

C   D   B   A

Circle the things whose names start with the letter A and underline the ones whose names start with the letter B.

Fill in the blanks to complete the names of the following objects.

A̲NTILOPE

d̲OLL

b̲EARD

C̲a̲KE

d̲OLPHIN

d̲UCK

b̲ROOM

A̲EROPLANE

A̲XE

E F G H

Match the following.

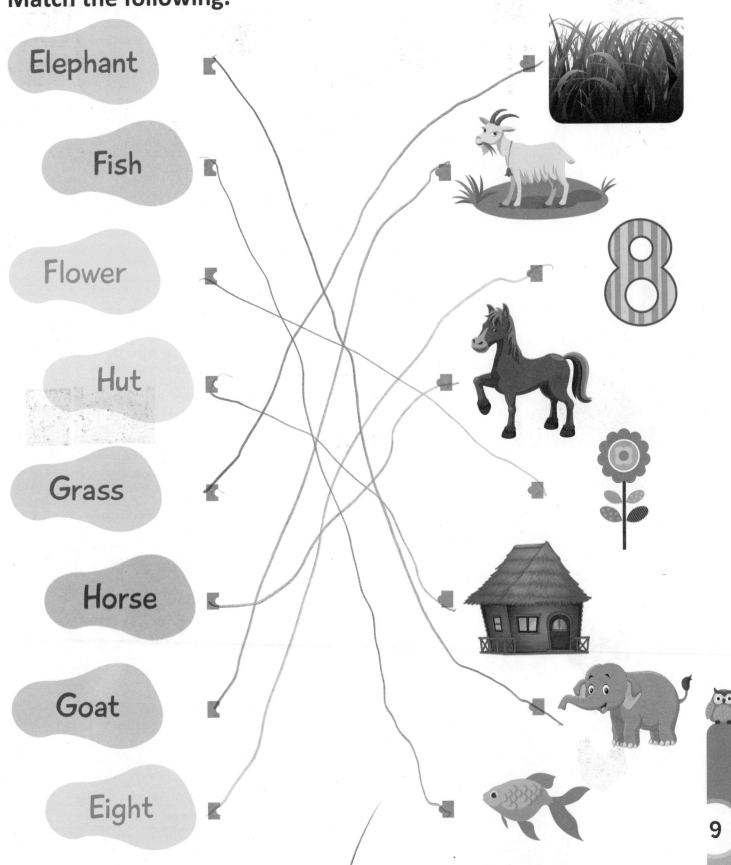

Elephant

Fish

Flower

Hut

Grass

Horse

Goat

Eight

Words

The names of these things start with the letter E or F. Name them and put them in the right box.

E	**F**
eggs Eye ear	Flower Five Frog

Look at the pictures and complete the following crossword.

Down:

1.  2.   3.

Across:

1.

3.

4.

				1.h	A	N	D
				O			
		2.G		U			
		O		S			
3.G	R	A	P	E	S		
a		t					
T							
E		4.h	E	N			

10

Fill in the blanks to complete the names of the following things.

F RO C K

EN g IN e

GL a SS e S

h UT

h i LL

G IFT

G LOB e

G i R L

Use the first alphabet of each word to make a new word. The first one has been done for you.

H U G = HUG

h O t = hot

G a p = Gap

E g g = egg

11

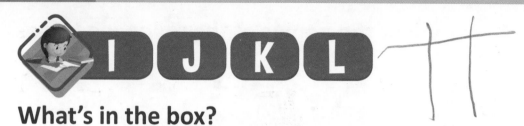

I J K L

What's in the box?

Lamp   Knot   Kite   Jug   Iron   Ice cube

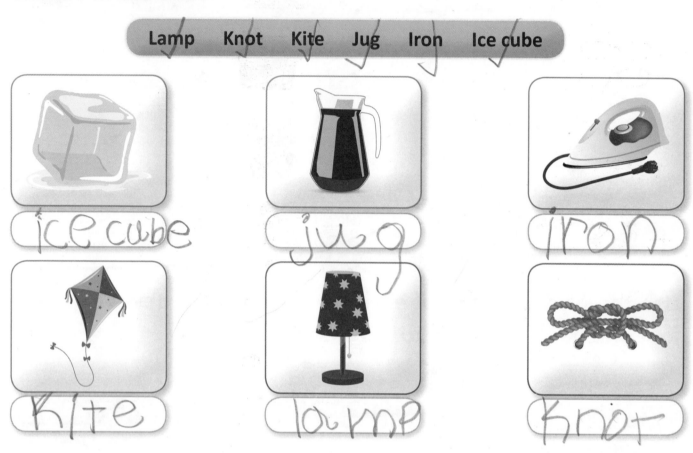

ice cube   jug   iron

kite   lamp   knot

Using the first alphabet of every picture, make a new word.

= IGLOO

(Hint: This is a house made of ice.)

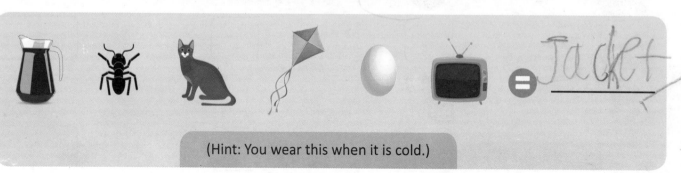

= Jacket

(Hint: You wear this when it is cold.)

12

= Joker

(Hint: A person who tells jokes.)

= ink

(Hint: We put this inside a pen to write.)

= Jungle

(Hint: This is where wild animals live.)

Try to make as many new words as you can from the following.
Remember, each word must have at least three letters.

KEYBOARD ➡ key, Board, day

ICE CREAM ➡ ice, cream, Rice, Armgram

JACKPOT ➡ tack, Pot, Jack

LADYBUG ➡ lady, buy, bay, bud, budy

Super

Look at the pictures and circle the right spellings.

(Lock)
Lok
Loke

Nife
Knif
(Knife)

Jeine
Jeens
(Jeans)

Ice creem
(Ice cream)
Ise cream

Kyng
Cing
(King)

Leef
Leafe
(Leaf)

Kangaru
(Kangaroo)
Kangroo

Legg
(Leg)
Lege

Iglu
(Igloo)
Egloo

Jokar
Jokir
(Joker)

Kee
(Key)
Kie

(Light)
Lit
Lite

Make new words using the letters in the hexagon. All words must use the alphabet L. Try to make a word using all the letters.

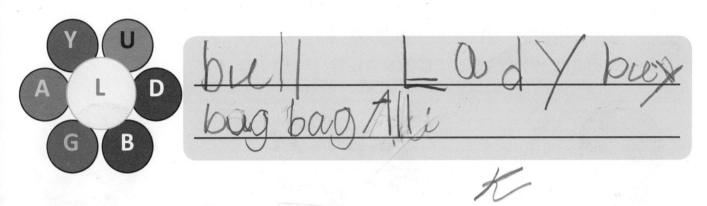

bull   Lady box ?
bag bag Alli

These words are missing a letter and you have two choices: k and l. So, take your pick and find the right fit.

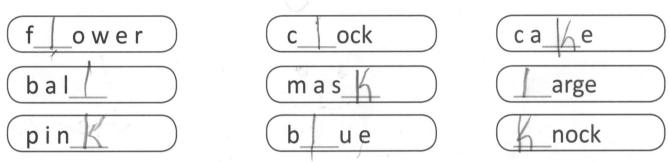

f l ower   c l ock   ca k e

b a l l   mas k   l arge

pin k   b l ue   k nock

The names of all these pictures all start with the letters i, j, k and l. Using the first alphabet of every picture, make a new word.

I ce cream   J oker   J elly

Igloo   Joke   Jam

K ite   K ayak   l ion

Kitten   Kkit   leaponding

15

M N O P

Fill in the blanks of the following objects. The names of the pictures start with the letters m, n, o and p.

mango

nest

orange

yogamat!

owl

nose

pencil

onion

pan

parrot

mouse

nine

COMPOUND WORDS

When you take two words and join them together to form a brand new word, it is called a compound word. For example: Rain + Bow = Rainbow.

From the column on the right side, circle the word you think would make a compound word.

Mail	Bake	Bond	(Box)
Make	Tell	Bill	(Up)
News	(Paper)	Bill	List
Pan	Brush	(Cake)	Top
Pony	Bat	Tall	(Tail)
Over	(Coat)	Seat	Bath
Neck	Ball	Work	(Lace)
Play	(Ground)	Box	Gate
Moon	Lift	(Light)	Lamp
Note	(Book)	Pen	Eraser
Pick	On	(Up)	For

There's something wrong with these words. Can you correct them and write the right spelling.

Opin _____open_____ (~~Open~~/Opun)

Onyun _____onion_____ (Union/~~Onion~~)

Paynt _____Paint_____ (~~Peint~~/Paint)

Oyl _____oil_____ (~~Oil~~/Oiel)

Pun _____Pen_____ (Pin/~~Pen~~)

Mauth _____mouth_____ (Mouth/~~Maoth~~)

Nite _____night_____ (Nitgh/~~Night~~)

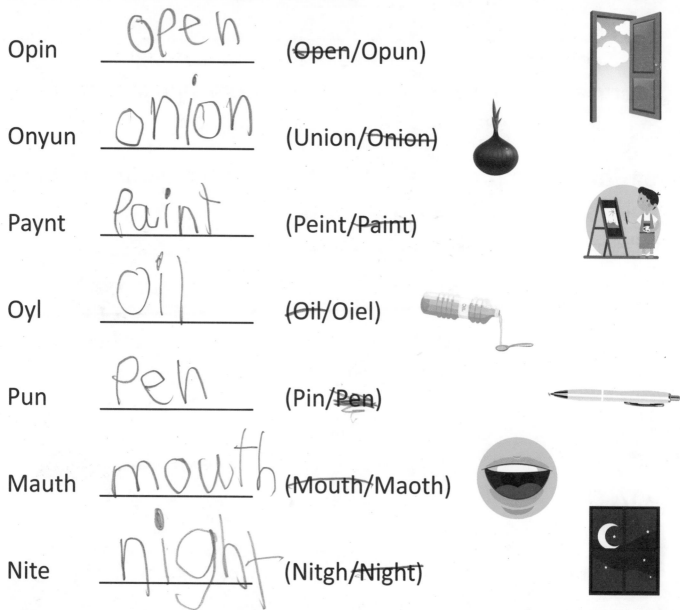

Make new words using the letters in the hexagon. Remember, all the words must use the letter P. Try to make a word using all the letters.

N U E P N I G

Pen Pin Pig Pie Pine

Q R S T

Find the following words in the word grid.

Quill   Rainbow   Roar   Row   Tree   Sun   Quiet   Snake   Tea   Reap

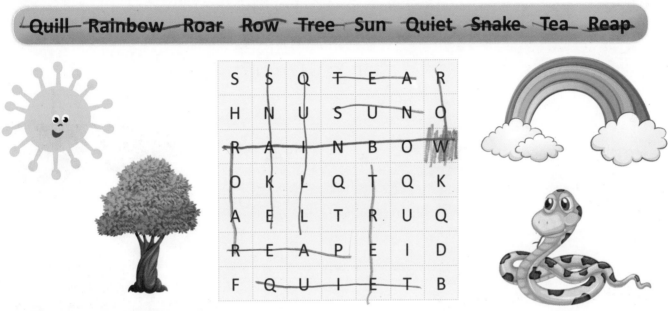

S S Q T E A R
H N U S U N O
R A I N B O W
O K L Q T Q K
A E L T R U Q
R E A P E I D
F Q U I E T B

What sounds like this?

In the left column is a list of words. In the right column, write words that sound like them. Make sure that these start with the letters Q, R, S or T.

Far	star
Sleep	sheep
White	right
Duck	truck
Built	quilt
Bun	fun
Habit	rabbit
Pain	rain

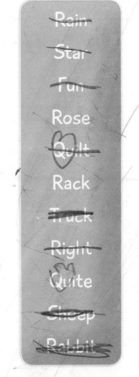

Rain
Star
Fun
Rose
Quilt
Rack
Truck
Right
Quite
Sheep
Rabbit

19

Look at the pictures and circle the right spellings.

Shu
Shoe
Shoo

Ring
Wring
Ringe

Rackt
Racket
Raykit

Tracter
Trectre
Tractor

soks
Socks
Soxc

Tigr
Tygre
Tiger

Rainbow
Reinbo
Ranebow

Quale
Queil
Quail

Sheep
Shiep
Shepe

Teddy
Tedy
Tady

Sixi
Sixe
Six

Rode
Rod
Road

Robote
~~Robot~~
~~Roabot~~

~~Queue~~
~~Quoe~~
~~Quoo~~

~~Trame~~
~~Traim~~
Tram

Swan
~~Svan~~
~~Swon~~

What's in the box? Name them.

tractor

three

Spoon

table

Star

Queen

bunny

ship

rope

Question

Soap

rocket

21

U V W X Y Z

Identify them and write the names in the right box.

U	V	W
Umbrella	Vase	Whale
Uniform	Van	Wheel
	Vest	Well

X	Y	Z
xray	Yak	Zipper
Xmas	YOLK	Zero
	Yellow	Zebra

Rearrange jumbled words and find out what they mean.

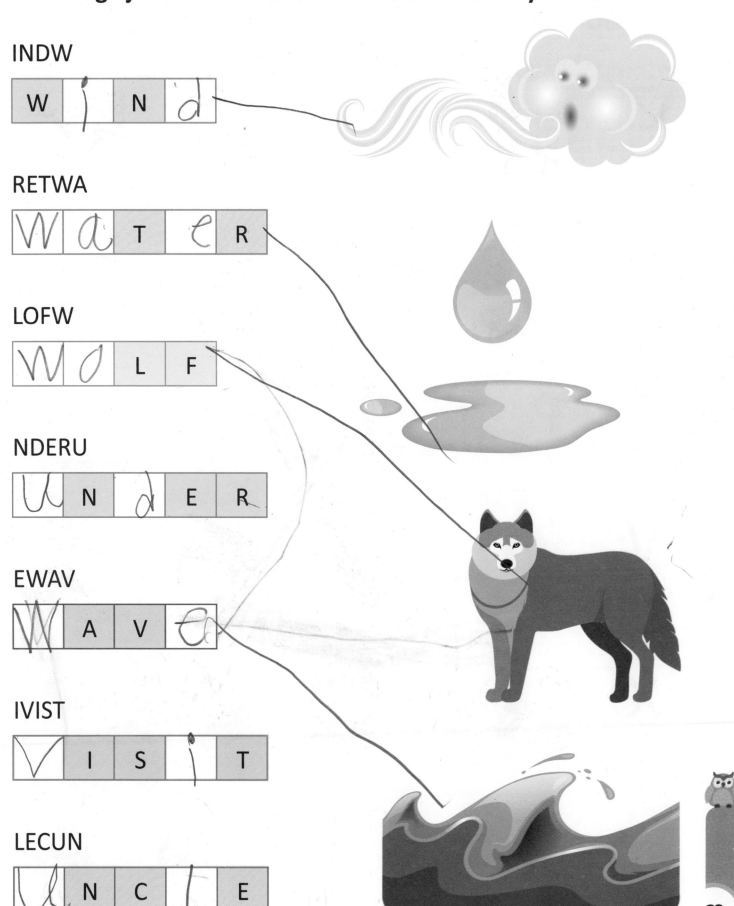

INDW

W	i	N	d

RETWA

W	a	T	e	R

LOFW

W	o	L	F

NDERU

U	N	d	E	R

EWAV

W		A	V	a

IVIST

V	I	S	i	T

LECUN

U	N	C	l	E

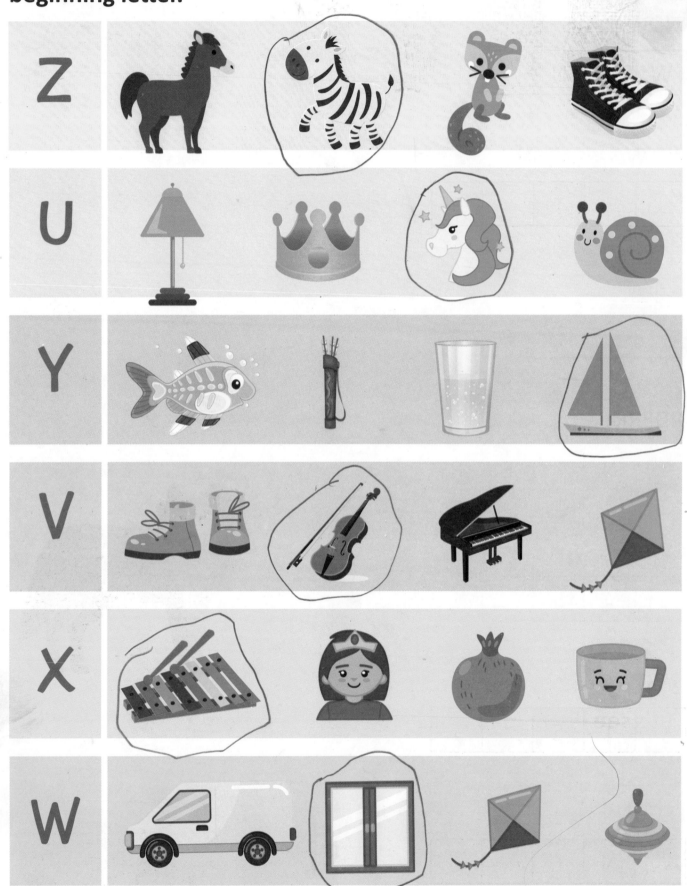

Words

Say the name of the each picture and circle it that matches the beginning letter.

24

Find the following words in the word grid.

X-Mas　　Yellow　　Yak　　Zebra　　Yes　　Zipper
Zero　　Your　　X-ray　　Year　　Xylophone　　Zigzag

X	R	T	Z	I	G	Z	A	G
U	H	S	E	Z	E	B	R	A
Y	O	U	R	I	Q	E	R	Y
X	Y	L	O	P	H	O	N	E
M	A	N	M	P	B	H	O	L
A	K	O	Y	E	S	B	G	L
S	Y	E	A	R	Z	E	R	O
V	D	P	F	X	R	A	Y	W

Let's see how many words can you make from YESTERDAY? Each word should have at least three letters.

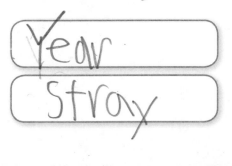

Year

Stray

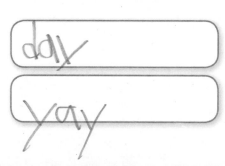

day

yay

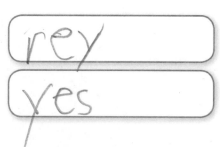

rey

yes

SIGHT WORDS

The sight words are frequently used words. They are recognized without sounding them.

Trace and learn the given list of sight words.

is	here	are	can	me	been
a	fig	in	my	has	over
the	she	had	too	him	off
I	small	to	not	was	like
have	this	do	bike	now	make
see	up	who	two	said	good
and	no	what	look	new	buy
an	it	at	come	wall	full
he	down	you	am	about	big
we	go	on	sit	wood	could

Find and circle the given sight words in the puzzle.

THAT	ON	ARE	HIM	TO
YOU	IT	FOR	NOW	OF

T	D	L	J	G	D	L	U	T	Y
S	U	E	G	I	I	Y	Y	E	E
J	Y	O	U	R	L	I	Z	A	L
A	R	E	S	M	S	B	M	J	L
W	O	F	A	T	H	A	T	N	O
T	O	H	W	M	N	Y	N	U	N
J	I	E	H	I	M	P	Y	B	W
U	Y	F	O	R	E	K	U	I	T
J	Y	R	T	F	N	O	W	I	H
Y	Z	B	R	J	Y	N	R	U	S

27

Fill in the blanks using the correct sight words.

and	the	his	was	for
as	he	is	in	with

Jim _____ Clara saw two cats.

Do _____ I say.

Edmund lost _____ wallet.

Thank you _____ coming.

Where _____ my toothbrush?

Keep _____ change.

_____ lost the match.

Dance _____ us.

I have chocolates _____ my bag.

How _____ the exam?

Read aloud the following sight words and write the question words in the blanks.

Read the word with and colour it. Then search the word in the box and circle it.

away   make   with

with   my   went   bat

I   need

with   at   that

find   a   help   jump

at   hat

at   big   at   jump   at

with

with

for

can   at

with   like

fat   not   with   play   see

to   the   with   are   at   in

for   you   for

with   the

with   it   and   at

RHYMING WORDS

Rhyming words are words that have the same ending sounds.

Match the picture with its correct rhyming word.

 •   • proud

 •   • truck

 •   • guest

 •   • down

 •   • feel

 •   • game

 •   • bun

 •   • fox

The words on the cards rhyme with sat. Now, look at the given pictures and write the correct rhyming word next to each picture.

_____

_____

_____

_____

32

Draw a line to match the pictures that have rhyming names.

Words

Underline the picture in each row that rhymes with the picture on the left.

34

Draw a line to match the words that rhyme with each other.

lake	tail
hut	cave
round	soon
wave	fly
sky	cone
bone	hump
jump	cool
pool	cake
moon	found
nail	but

Look at each picture. Fill in the word that rhymes with the bold word given in each sentence.

The _____ has a **toy**.

The **mouse** ran into the _____.

The **man** cooked omelette in the _____.

The _____ rang near the **well**.

The _____ jumped on the **log**.

Tom has some **sand** in his _____.

PHONICS

SOUND WORDS

Phonics refers to anything that is related to sound. We can learn to read and spell words correctly with the help of phonics.

Say ant. The word ant begins with the A sound. Circle the pictures that begin with A sound using your favourite crayon.

Say bee. The word bee begins with the B sound. Match the following words that have the B sound with correct pictures.

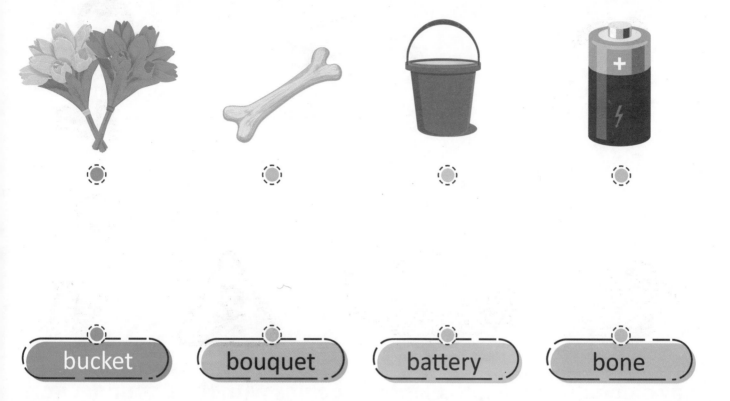

bucket   bouquet   battery   bone

Say cat. The word cat begins with the C sound. Colour the cards of pictures that begin with the C sound.

Say **duck**. The word **duck** begins with the **D** sound. Draw a line from **D** to the pictures that have the **D** sound.

Say **elephant**. The word **elephant** begins with the **E** sound. Circle the pictures that begin with the **E** sound using your favourite crayon.

Say food. The word food begins with the F sound. Write the names under the pictures that begin with the F sound.

_____

_____

_____

_____

_____

_____

_____

_____

_____

Say grass. The word grass begins with the G sound. Colour the cards of pictures that have the G sound.

Say horse. The word **horse** begins with the **H** sound. Draw a line from the letter **H** to the pictures that begin with **H** sound.

Say igloo. The word **igloo** begins with the **I** sound. Circle the pictures that have the **I** sound using your favourite crayon.

Say jar. The word jar begins with the J sound. Now, look at the objects given below and colour the pictures that have the J sound.

Say kettle. The word kettle begins with the K sound. Draw a line from K to the pictures that have the K sound.

Say lock. The word lock begins with the L sound. Match the following words that have the L sound.

leaf

lock

lamp

lion

lizard

lemon

45

Say mouse. The word mouse begins with the M sound. Colour the cards of pictures that have the M sound.

Say newspaper. The word newspaper begins with the N sound. Circle the pictures that have the N sound using your favourite crayon.

Say octopus. The word octopus begins with the O sound. Draw a line from O to the pictures that have the O sound.

Say parrot. The word parrot begins with the P sound. Now, match the pictures with the P sound words.

panda

penguin

pen

popcorn

pot

pillow

47

Say quail. The word quail begins with the Q sound. Match the following words that have the Q sound.

queen

question

quilt

quill

quack

quiet

Say rabbit. The word rabbit begins with the R sound. Circle the pictures that have the R sound using your favourite crayon.

Say sky. The word sky begins with the S sound. Tick (✓) the pictures that begin with the S sound.

Say turtle. The word turtle begins with the T sound. Draw a line from T to the pictures that have the T sound.

Say **uncle**. The word **uncle** begins with the **U** sound. Now, look at the objects given below and colour the objects that have the **U** sound.

Say **violin**. The word **violin** begins with the **V** sound. Now, match the pictures to the **V** sound words.

vase

van

vest

violin

vegetables

vulture

Say wall. The word wall begins with the W sound. Tick (✓) mark the pictures that have the W sound.

Say x-ray. The word x-ray begins with the X sound. Colour the pictures that have the X sound.

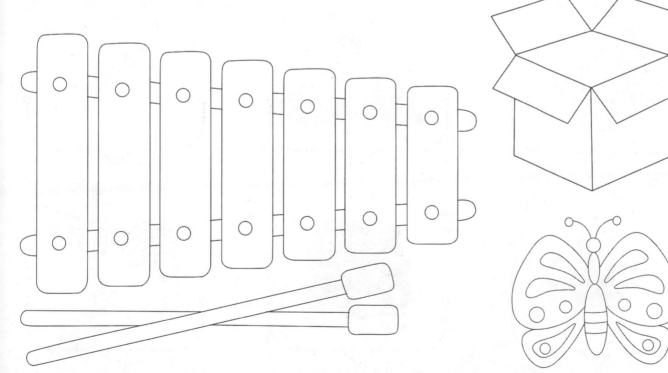

Say yo-yo. Draw a line from Y to the pictures that begin with the Y sound.

Say zebra. The word zebra begins with the Z sound. Colour the cards of pictures that have the Z sound.

VOWELS

Look at the pictures and fill in the missing vowels to complete the words.

_rtist

_ndia

peng_in

bask_t

drag_n

Short a

The letter **a** is a vowel. It has two sounds: the **short a** sound like apple and **long a** sound like cake.

Read aloud the words for each picture. Circle the pictures that have the **short a** sound.

Long a

Complete each sentence using the **long a** words given in the box.

May, maze, grapes, paint, ape

We saw an _____ in the zoo.

Stella's birthday is in _____.

Can we play the _____ game?

Mike like to draw and _____

His mother bought _____ and mangoes from the market.

Short e

The letter e is a vowel. It has two sounds: the short e sound like elbow and long e sound like bee.

Read aloud the words for each picture. Circle the pictures that have the short e sound.

55

Long e

Complete each sentence using the long e words given in the splashes.

wheel queen bee cheese feet

The _____  might sting you.

Liza has pretty _____ .

Tom loves to eat _____ .

The _____ is wearing a beautiful crown.

A _____ is round.

Short i

The letter i is a vowel. It has two sounds: the short i sound like ink and long i sound like ice.

Read aloud the words for each picture. Circle the pictures that have the short i sound.

Long i

Complete each sentence using the long i words given in the circles.

 kite  ice  tie   iron  island

Charles flies a _____.

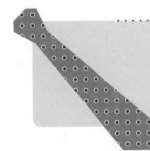 David has a lovely _____.

Jack is going to an _____.

 Do not touch the _____.
It is hot.

There is an _____ cube
in the mug.

Short o

The letter o is a vowel. It has two sounds: the short o sound like orange and long o sound like ocean.

Read aloud the words for each picture. Circle the pictures that have the short o sound.

Long o

Complete each sentence using the long o words given in the clouds.

bone boat coat toad cone

Grandpa wears a _____.

Norah likes to eat ice cream in a _____.

The dog has a _____.

The _____ floats on the water.

The _____ jumps into the pool.

Short u

The letter u is a vowel. It has two sounds: the short u sound like up and long u sound like uniform.

Read aloud the words for each picture. Circle the pictures that have the short u sound.

Long u

Complete each sentence using the long u words given in the balloons.

blue cute flute huge uniform

Peter has a _____ cat in his hand.

Sam needs the _____ stool to hang the picture.

Katie's brother gifted her a _____ .

The _____ elephant is in the zoo.

My mum has bought a new _____ for my sister.

CONSONANTS

Now, let's learn about consonants. Colour the box which has a consonant in it using your favourite crayon.

o	c	h	i	v	k
n	a	x	d	e	y
z	e	t	d	y	a
o	s	i	e	y	p
j	l	a	k	i	e
n	a	p	j	u	q
d	v	f	l	k	o
m	o	w	i	u	g

All the pictures given below start with the consonants **b**, **c**, **d** or **f**. Write the letters and say the name. What sound does each letter make?

___ rum   ___ rog   ___ row

___ ace   ___ angle   ___ oll

All the pictures given below start with the consonants **g**, **h**, **j** or **k**. Write the letters and say the name. What sound does each letter make?

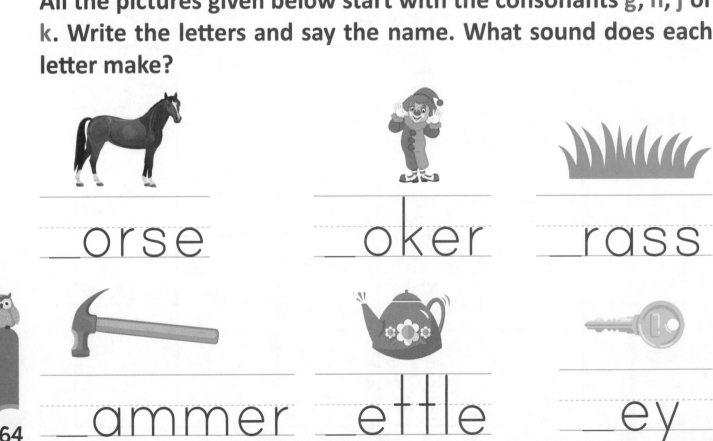

___ orse   ___ oker   ___ rass

___ ammer   ___ ettle   ___ ey

64

All the pictures given below start with the consonants l, m, or n. Write the letters and say the name. What sound does each letter make?

__ose   __onkey   __emon

__adder   __agnet   __ails

All the pictures given below start with the consonants p, q or r. Write the letters and say the name. What sound does each letter make?

__aint   __ake   __arrot

__uilt   __ainbow   __ueen

All the pictures given below start with the consonants s, t or v. Write the letters and say the name. What sound does each letter make?

<u>_</u>tar　　　<u>_</u>able　　　<u>_</u>nake

<u>_</u>iolin　　　<u>_</u>urtle　　　<u>_</u>ase

All the pictures given below start with the consonants w, x, y or z. Write the letters and say the name. What sound does each letter make?

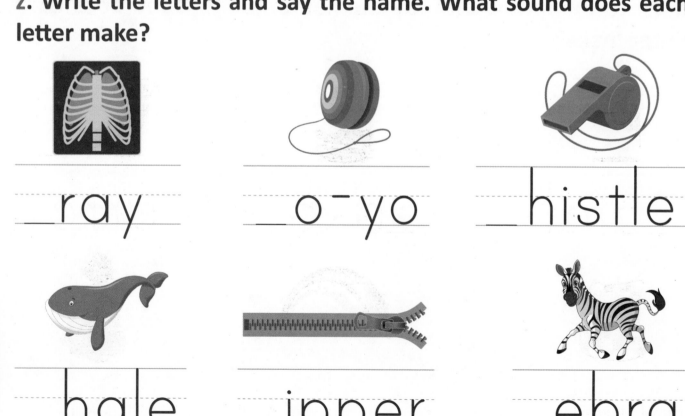

<u>_</u>ray　　　<u>_</u>o-yo　　　<u>_</u>histle

<u>_</u>hale　　　<u>_</u>ipper　　　<u>_</u>ebra

66

The consonant c has two sounds - hard like cat and soft like city.

Match the objects to the correct sounds.

The consonant g has two sounds - hard like glass and soft like gym.

Match the objects to the correct sounds.

SPECIAL SOUND WORDS-1

CH, SH, PH, TH, WH

From the pictures, find out which words start with ch, sh, ph, th or wh. Then write their names below.

Ch	
Sh	
Ph	
Wh	
Th	

Find the missing sound.

Mash   Chest   Then   That   Rush   Short   Church   With

		E	S	T

W	I		

M	A		

		E	N

	U		

		A	T

		O	R	T

	U	R	

69

SPECIAL SOUND WORDS-2

CR, BR, DR, FR, GR

Complete the following words with Cr, Br, Dr, Fr, or Gr.

_ _ead   _ _own   _ _ass   _ _og

_ _agon   _ _ame   _ _apes   _ _ab

Write the names of the following.

_____ _____ _____ _____

_____ _____ _____ _____

VOCABULARY

THREE LETTER WORDS

Change the first letter and make a new word.

CUT → BUT

PEN → _____

HIP → _____

FAN → _____

SEE → _____

MAT → _____

BAT → _____

KIT → _____

HUT → _____

JUG → _____

RAT → _____

RUT → _____

BIN → _____

ROW → _____

COT → _____

JET → _____

Change the last letter and make a new word.

TAP → TAN

LID → _____

HIS → _____

BIN → _____

MEN → _____

PAY → _____

DIG → _____

PEA → _____

BUN → _____

PIT → _____

TON → _____

RUB → _____

CAP → _____

FIR → _____

BEE → _____

FIG → _____

Rearrange the letters in correct order to make a word.

AET	EAP
GBA	INT
TPO	YKE
ADY	RTA
RCA	GEG
HTO	WLO
TNO	UTH
PNE	UBT

Find the given words in the word search and circle them.

get pet jet met

pot dot mop top

I	C	Q	P	O	T	I
G	B	M	E	T	H	L
A	F	E	D	J	E	T
P	G	O	N	D	O	T
E	E	M	O	P	J	K
T	T	P	G	T	O	P

Match the words with the pictures.

Ship

Pineapple

Cane

Milk

Camel

Cake

Star

Book

76

FOUR LETTER WORDS

Rearrange the letters to make words.

TBAH ▷

NOES ▷

AMNI ▷

BTEU ▷

ENIN ▷

CIED ▷

GAET ▷

ETTN ▷

ATBE ▷

MFOA ▷

ABDN ▷

PHAT ▷

ETTS ▷

PLEH ▷

KCUD ▷

EERT ▷

YALC ▷

IRCE ▷

RDCO ▷

DEKS ▷

Match the similar words with their pictures.

 Cook

 Boot

 Look

 Wood

 Root

 Hook

 Foot

SYNONYMS

Synonyms are words that mean the same.

Choose the matching synonyms from the words given in the box and write down.

chef, large, rock, happy, street, little, ill, angry, sad

cook

annoyed

sick

huge

road

stone

joy

tiny

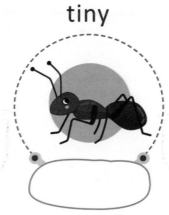

unhappy

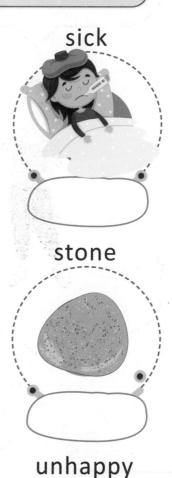

79

Tick (✓) the correct option.

glad   sad

kid   boy

pond   ocean

soft   hard

man   woman

fat   thin

Complete the given spelling sums. Now, find these action words in the grid and circle them.

G + ive = ...

W + eep = ...

W + ere = ...

S + aid = ...

H + ate = ...

A + ct = ...

W	E	E	P	Z	H	A	N	G
W	G	S	R	W	A	S	K	G
A	I	A	I	E	T	E	A	R
S	V	I	C	R	E	E	C	I
K	E	D	K	E	S	E	T	P

A + sk = ...

T + ear = ...

H + ang = ...

S + ee = ...

G + rip = ...

P + rick = ...

81

ANTONYMS

Antonyms are words that mean the opposites.

Find the words from the clouds and write in the blanks next to its antonyms.

girl

exit

sell

wet

west

bad

hard

dirty

weak

old

boy	_____	enter	_____
good	_____	clean	_____
soft	_____	strong	_____
dry	_____	young	_____
buy	_____	east	_____

Fill the vowels- a, e, i, o, u in the blanks and complete the words.

j__mp	p__rk	b__ll
m__ke	r__ng	d__st
b__nk	b__nd	n__st
tw__	__rm	b__st

Fill the consonants- n, p, q, r, s, t in the blanks and complete the words.

__ear	__orch	__ink
__uiet	__ong	__rize
__ight	__ofa	__ocket
__uest	__ush	__hoes

Colour the correct spelling in each row.

beek	beak	bik	beik
haf	hafe	half	halfe
wing	weng	ving	wieng
rast	rest	raste	resta
tiem	tim	time	tyme

Make new words.

Make words ending -ell

_____

Make words ending -ock

_____

Make words ending -ut

_____

Make words ending -ick

_____

Make words ending -ay

_____

Complete these words by filling letter a, b, c or d.

__ox

__awl

fl__g

__ulb

d__rk

h__ir

__irty

__loth

__ald

o__ean

__ad

fl__g

go__t

__ud

__lue

__asket

__ell

__ag

__ath

__uy

l__mb

__lack

cr__b

__ark

__loud

b__nk

__lose

85

Rearrange the letters to make words starting with F and N.

AEFC = _____

TESN = _____

NILA = _____

SONE = _____

CKEN = _____

NEEELD = _____

ROKF = _____

RIFE = _____

TKAN = _____

VEFI = _____

FXO = _____

TFEE = _____

OFDO = _____

MATHS

MISSING NUMBERS

Write the missing numbers in the box.

13	14	15	16	17	18	19	20
30	31	32	33	34	35	36	37
38	39	10	11	12	13	14	15
46	47	48	49	50	51	52	53
75	76	77	78	79	80	81	82
54	55	56	57	58	59	60	61
62	63	24	25	26	27	28	29
90	91	92	93	94	95	96	97
84	85	86	87	88	89	90	91
92	93	66	67	68	69	70	71

BACKWARD COUNTING

Write the backward counting.

21 — 20 — 19 — 18 — 17 — 16 — 15 — 14

19 — 18 — 17 — 16 — 15 — 14 — 13 — 12

31 — 30 — 29 — 28 — 27 — 26 — 25 — 24

16 — 15 — 14 — 13 — 12 — 11 — 10 — 9

47 — 46 — 45 — 44 — 43 — 42 — 41 — 40

62 — 61 — 60 — 59 — 58 — 57 — 56 — 55

70 — 69 — 68 — 67 — 66 — 65 — 64 — 63

100 — 99 — 98 — 97 — 96 — 95 — 94 — 93

54 — 53 — 52 — 51 — 50 — 49 — 48 — 47

80 — 79 — 78 — 77 — 76 — 75 — 74 — 73

COUNTING

Count the number of objects and tick (✓) the correct number.

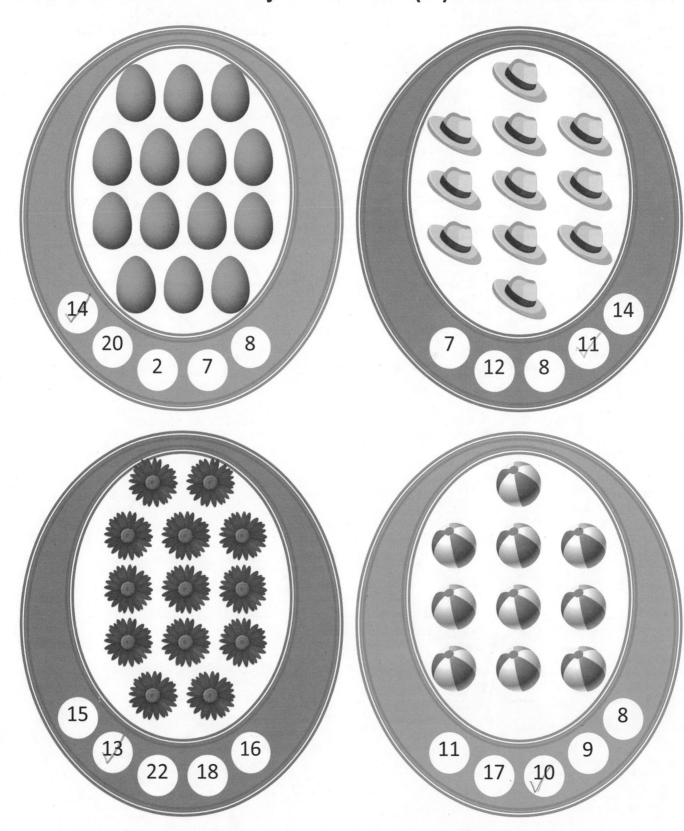

MIRROR IMAGE

There are a few mirror images of numbers. They are inverted, but some of them look same. Write them correctly.

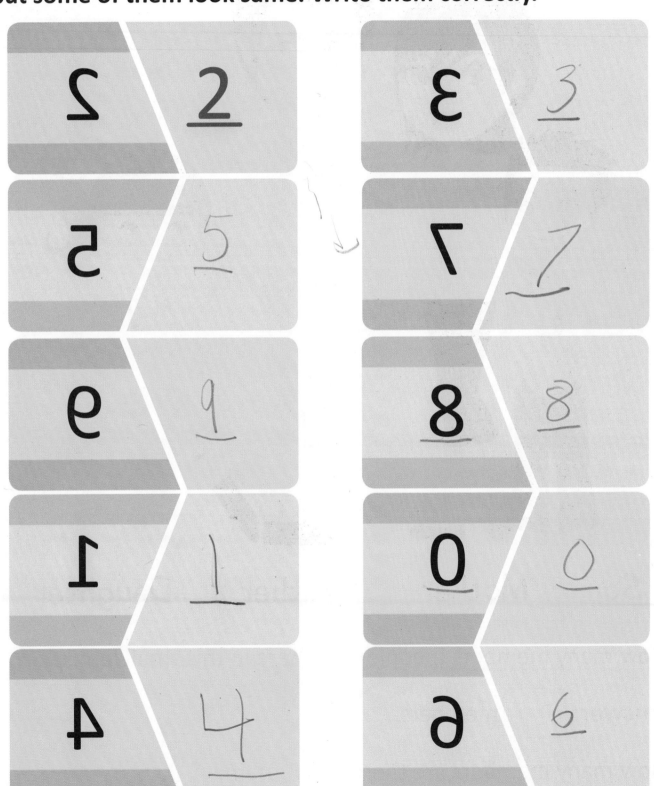

MEMBERS IN A FAMILY

Son   Mother   Father   Daughter

 How many members (people) are there in this small family?

Answer: 4 members.

How many members are there in your family? 5

NUMBER NAMES

Circle the number names in the word search puzzle.

A P Q O N E Z T B M T R A T A N

C S I X D F G K O W H C R W S F

H A R E N M W R H R R E N O N A

N I N E Q L K B S H E E E D E O

J Q E V D N S R E K E P O S I X

A T W O O T E N F O Q S U I N E

T G N A P C X T G P F R E L F E

O N I N E T W E N T Y S I X O O

F G T W E L V E T E V L G I U R

O H E N O N E P O F E I H O R E

U S N T S E V E N F I F T E E N

EVEN NUMBERS

Given below is a chessboard.

There are five figures. Tick (✓) the correct shape of the chessboard.

Write the missing even and odd numbers.

1	2	3	4	5	6	7	8
9	10	11	12	13	14	15	16
17	18	19	20	21	22	23	24
25	26	27	28	29	30	31	32
33	34	35	36	37	38	39	40
41	42	43	44	45	46	47	48
49	50	51	52	53	54	55	56
57	58	59	60	61	62	63	64

Remember

- Even numbers have 2, 4, 6, 8 or 0 in the end.
- Even numbers can be exactly divided by 2.
- Odd numbers can not be divided by 2.

ADDITION

Count and add.

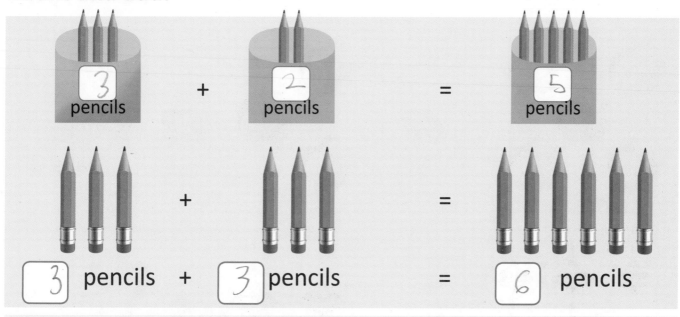

$\boxed{3}$ pencils $+$ $\boxed{3}$ pencils $=$ $\boxed{6}$ pencils

Add and see how many balloons you have. Then colour the total number of balloons.

$\boxed{2}$ balloons $+$ $\boxed{3}$ balloons $=$ $\boxed{5}$ balloons

Count and draw the number of candles you need to add to get 5 candles in all.

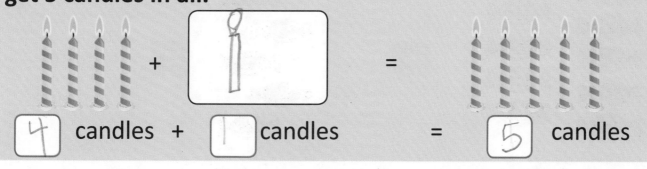

$\boxed{4}$ candles $+$ $\boxed{1}$ candles $=$ $\boxed{5}$ candles

SUBTRACTION

Count and subtract.

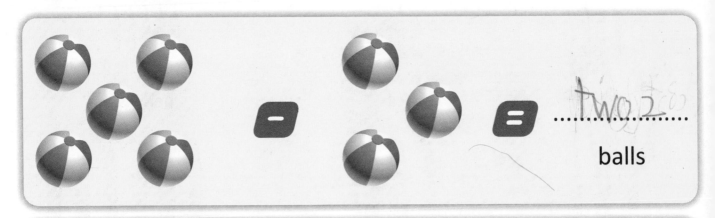

two 2 — balls

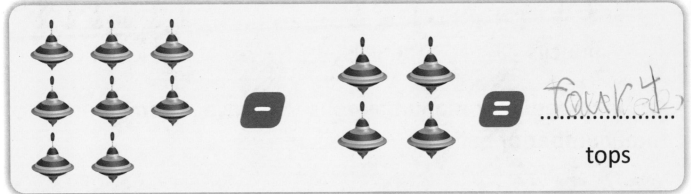

four 4 — tops

three 3 — caps

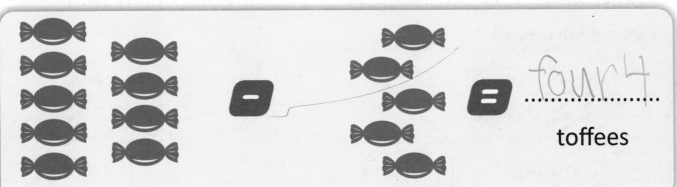

four 4 — toffees

Find the total.

 + 8 + Two = **15**

 + 6 + Five = 13

 + 7 + Six = 16

 + 6 + Three = 15

 + 9 + Four = 17

 + 6 + Seven = 21

 + 10 + One = 15

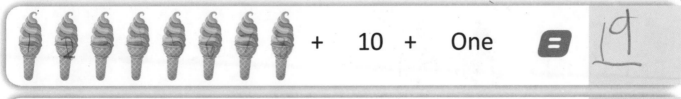 + 10 + One = 19

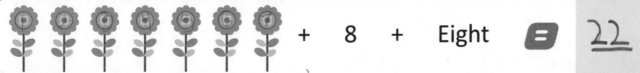 + 8 + Eight = 22

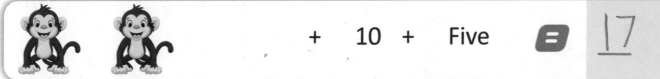 + 10 + Five = 17

Find the total.

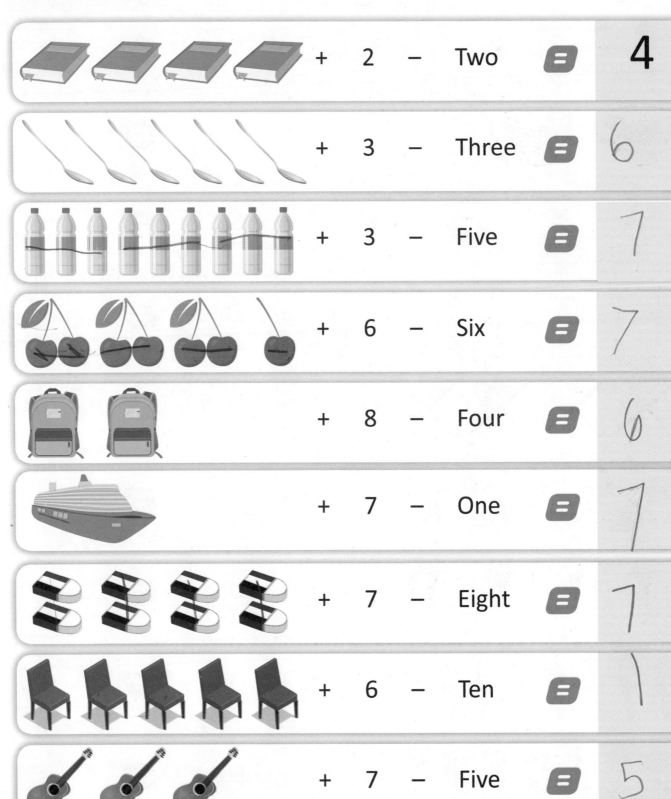

📚📚📚📚	+ 2	–	Two	= **4**
🥄🥄🥄🥄🥄🥄	+ 3	–	Three	= 6
🍾🍾🍾🍾🍾🍾🍾🍾🍾	+ 3	–	Five	= 7
🍒🍒🍒🍒	+ 6	–	Six	= 7
🎒🎒	+ 8	–	Four	= 6
🚢	+ 7	–	One	= 7
💊💊💊💊	+ 7	–	Eight	= 7
🪑🪑🪑🪑🪑	+ 6	–	Ten	= 1
🎸🎸🎸	+ 7	–	Five	= 5
🎎🎎🎎🎎	+ 9	–	Seven	= 6

COMPARISON

Big and Small

 Bird is small.

 Elephant is big.

Tick (✓) the object which is big.

Tick (✓) the bigger object, cross (x) the smaller object in each set.

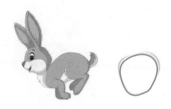

Tall and Short

Write T for tall and S for short in each set.

Near and Far

Look at the picture. Tick (✓) the object which is near the boy and cross (x) the one which is far away.

Tick (✓) which is near the man and cross (x) which is far.

On and Under

Tick (✓) the correct option in the brackets.

The (book/bag) is on the table.

The (book/bag) is under the table.

Top, Middle and Bottom

Look at the pictures carefully, then answer the following questions.

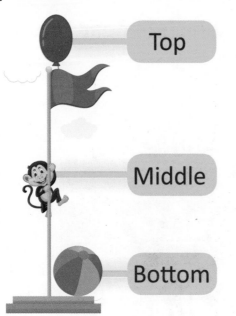

Top	What is at the top?	baloon
Middle	What is in the middle?	monkey
Bottom	What is at the bottom?	balls

Draw a cherry on top of the cake.

Draw pebbles at the bottom of the bucket.

SHACPES

Write the names of the shapes.

triangle, square, circle, oval, star, rectangle, diamond, hexagon, pentagon

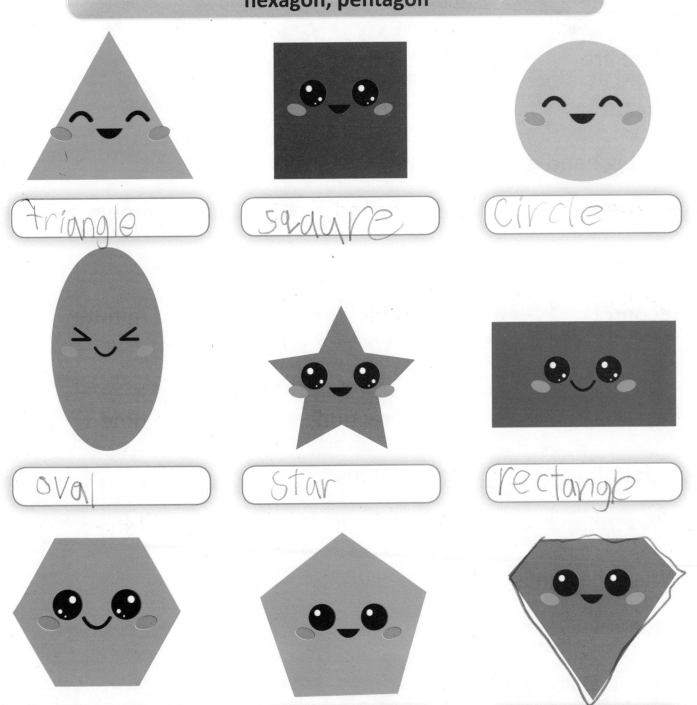

triangle

sqaure

circle

oval

star

rectangle

hexegon

pentogon

diamond

 **TIME ZONE**

Tick (✓) the correct option and fill in the blanks.

A day has __24__ hours.

23 ◯   24 ✓   25 ◯

There are __60__ seconds in a minute.

50 ◯   60 ✓   70 ◯

The big hand of a clock is the __minute__ hand.

minute ✓   second ◯   hour ◯

The small hand of a clock shows __hour__ .

second ◯   hour ✓   minute ◯

The clock helps to know the __time__ .

day ◯   direction ◯   time ✓

A clock has __12__ numbers.

12 ✓   13 ◯   14 ◯

When the sun is high in the sky, it is __noon__ .

noon ✓   night ◯   evening ◯

We see stars in the sky at __night__ .

noon ◯   morning ◯   night ✓

MY WORLD

HOME

Match the given objects to the places where they are found.

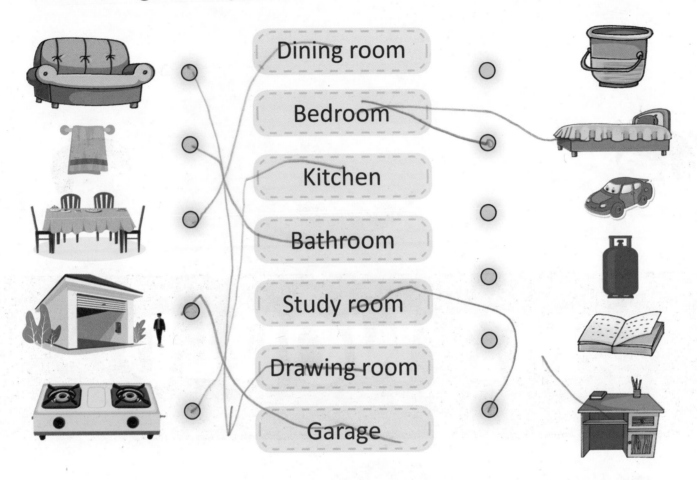

Dining room

Bedroom

Kitchen

Bathroom

Study room

Drawing room

Garage

Solve the crossword puzzle with the help of picture clues.

Match the following.

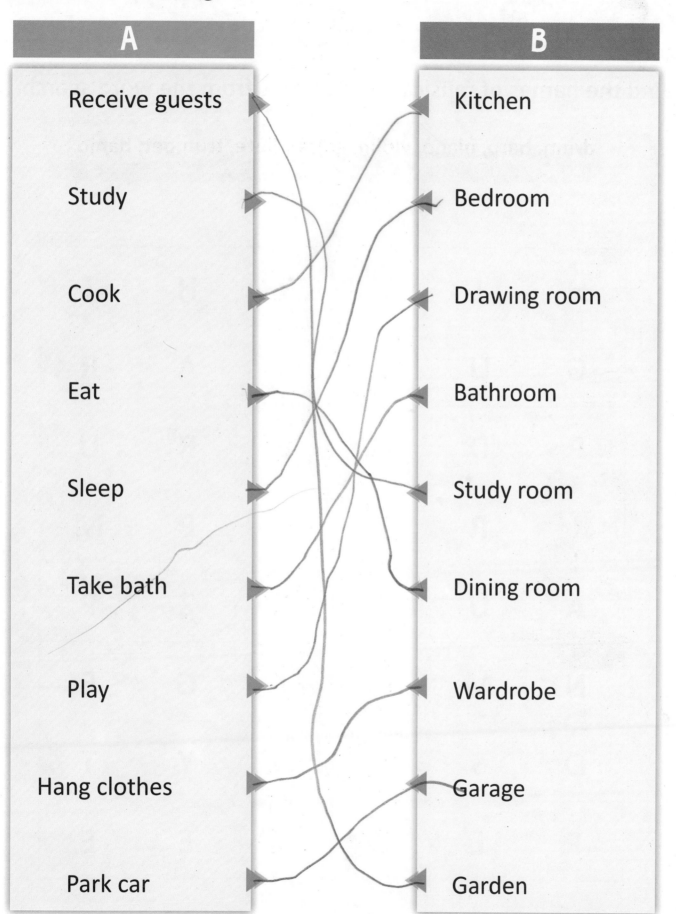

A	B
Receive guests	Kitchen
Study	Bedroom
Cook	Drawing room
Eat	Bathroom
Sleep	Study room
Take bath	Dining room
Play	Wardrobe
Hang clothes	Garage
Park car	Garden

MUSICAL INSTRUMENTS

Find the names of musical instruments from the word search.

drum, harp, piano, violin, guitar, flute, trumpet, banjo

H	J	V	Y	H	T
G	U	I	T	A	R
P	D	O	B	R	U
I	R	L	A	P	M
A	U	I	N	Z	P
N	M	N	J	G	E
O	S	A	O	Y	T
F	L	U	T	E	E

COMMUNITY HELPERS

Write names of the community helpers.

plumber, doctor, postman, teacher, farmer, chemist, tailor, carpenter, cobbler

The names of four helpers are hidden in the word search puzzle given below. Circle them.

J	T	E	A	C	H	E	R
S	G	E	H	H	N	R	O
K	K	L	C	E	S	D	S
R	P	E	N	M	E	R	L
K	G	T	A	I	L	O	R
B	N	W	T	S	L	I	R
M	E	R	D	T	G	X	S
S	A	I	Z	X	J	P	O
L	T	C	N	O	T	V	S
D	O	C	T	O	R	S	D

The pictures of some animals carrying balloons with a letter written on it are given below. Arrange these letters and see what word you get.

Circle the odd one out.

A doctor needs.

A teacher needs.

A butcher needs.

A sweeper needs.

A florist needs.

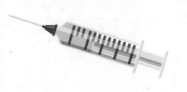   

NEIGHBOURHOOD PLACES

You have seen many shops in your neighbourhood. Match the given items with the shops where you can find these items.

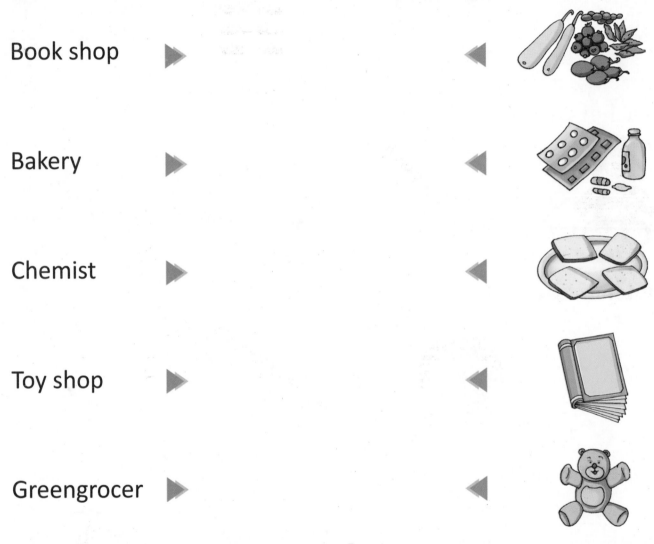

Book shop ▶ ◀

Bakery ▶ ◀

Chemist ▶ ◀

Toy shop ▶ ◀

Greengrocer ▶ ◀

Identify the given pictures and write their names. The first letter is given to you.

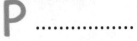

P ....   H ....   M ....   F ....

FOOD

**Circle the names of the food items in the word search puzzle.
Use the picture clues to do so.**

P	S	H	N	M	L	P	F	S
O	F	M	A	N	G	O	W	D
T	H	J	A	C	R	I	C	E
A	C	V	B	E	A	N	S	H
T	A	X	A	L	P	E	A	M
O	R	H	N	B	E	J	D	G
F	R	F	A	A	S	W	B	L
Q	O	C	N	B	P	I	D	M
J	T	D	A	P	P	L	E	W

   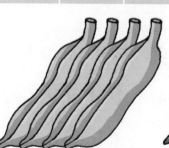 

HEALTH FIRST

Choose the correct word from the fruit basket and fill in the blanks.

_____ makes us healthy and strong.

We get fruits and vegetables from _____.

Milk makes our bones and teeth _____.

We should not eat lot of _____.

We get eggs from _____.

Put a tick (✓) for correct statements and a cross (x) for the wrong statement.

Healthy food makes us weak.

We should overeat.

We should not waste food.

We should eat lot of chips and candies.

We should eat fresh and clean fruits and vegetables.

CLOTHES

Look at the pictures. Write 'S' in the box for the clothes we wear in Summer and 'W' for the clothes we wear in Winter.

115

Choose the correct option and fill in the blanks.

We wear _____ clothes in summer. (cotton/woollen)

_____ clothes keep us warm in winter. (Cotton/Woollen)

We get _____ from sheep. (cotton/wool)

We get cotton from _____. (sheep/plant)

We wear _____ to protect ourselves from rain. (raincoat/swimming suit)

Cotton clothes keep our body _____. (hot/cool)

Look at the given pictures and write their names in the correct columns given below.

Sweater   Skirt   Muffler   Shorts   Shirt

Umbrella   Woollen Cap   Raincoat   Gumboots

Summer season	Winter season	Rainy season

GAMES

Tick (✓) the indoor games and cross (x) the outdoor games.

GROUP THINGS

Circle the odd one out in each row.

STAY TOGETHER

Match them with their pairs.

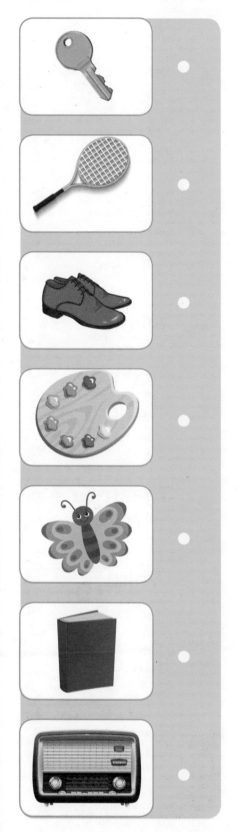

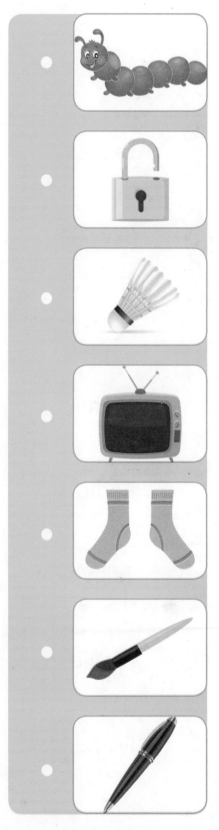

119

Match the following.

Rose	Dark
Sun Flower	Green
Leaves	Pond
Sky	Flower
Milk	Yellow
Night	Music
Radio	Theatre
Television	White
Movie	Rainbow
Fish	Cartoon

SCIENCE

PARTS OF A PLANT

Find the following words in the word search grid.

| Plant | Leaves | Oxygen | Stem | Root | Taproot | Fruit | Seed |

Q	W	S	E	E	D	R	O	O	T
N	P	L	A	N	T	M	D	O	P
Z	X	E	W	Q	A	K	L	X	B
A	S	A	F	G	P	J	K	Y	U
X	N	V	K	L	R	P	I	G	L
S	T	E	M	Y	O	U	N	E	B
Q	G	S	D	J	O	H	C	N	S
F	F	R	U	I	T	I	Z	E	R

Circle the correct option from the following.

It is the smallest part of the plant.

| seed | flower | leaf | stem |

It keeps the plant upright.

| seed | flower | leaf | stem |

It is generally green in colour.

| seed | flower | leaf | stem |

It is the part of the plant that has fragrance.

| seed | flower | leaf | stem |

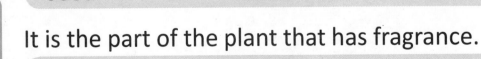

Chimpu monkey is throwing mangoes from the tree. Help Della to find the right mango to place in the given blanks.

(Clue: Read the words written on the mango)

Seed   Leaf   Roots   Stem

The _____ prepares food for the plant.

The _____ absorbs water and
mineral from the soil.

Fruits have _____ inside them.

The _____ helps the plant to stand straight.

Some letters are given in the tree below. Using those letters write the names of the parts of a plant. You can use each letter more than once.

T
D
E W S
O
U
L I M R F
L
A

PHOTOSYNTHESIS

The process by which plants make their food is called photosynthesis. Look at the picture and answer why plants cannot make their food during the night?

Because _____ light is not there at night.

SOLAR POWER

Power can be generated by wind, water, coal and solar (sun's) energy etc. Help the wind reach the turbine so that it can work.

NATURAL AND MAN-MADE

Tick (✓) the things given below that are not invented by the scientists.

Divide the natural and the man-made things in two columns.

Natural	Man-made		Natural	Man-made

FRUITS CROSSWORD

Look at the fruits given below. Fill in the box and find their names.

PLANTS AND ANIMALS

Write (P) in the given box for the things we get from plants and (A) for the things we get from animals.

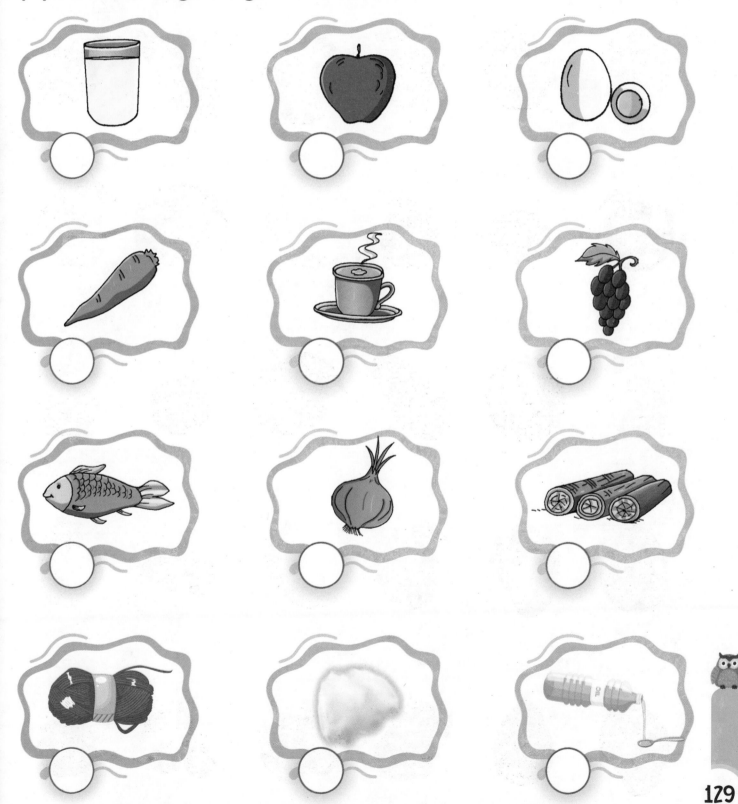

 # FRUITS WITH SEEDS

Tick (✓) the correct options.

Fruits with one seed.

Fruits with few seeds.

Fruits with many seeds.

Fruits with no seeds.

Fruits with its seeds on the outside.

WATER IS PRECIOUS

Tick (✓) the correct option.

We use water for

Where do we get water from?

Which of these do not need water?

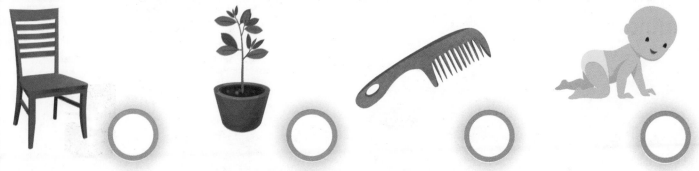

In our homes, we store drinking water in

Put a cross (x) in the box given beside the picture showing wastage of water.

SOLID AND LIQUID

Some of these pictures show things that are solid. Write 'S' under the pictures that are solid. Write 'L' under those that are liquid.

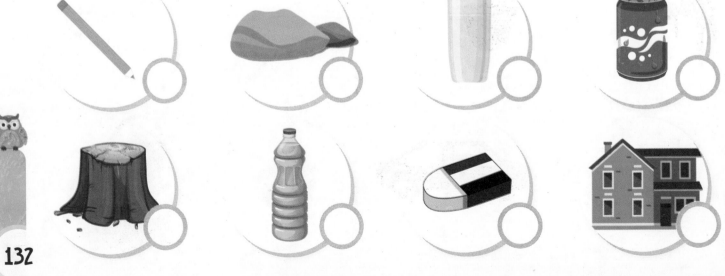

FLOAT AND SINK

Tick (✓) the things that can float on water. Cross (x) the things that will sink in water.

WIND

The name of some things that move with the help of wind is given here. Unjumble the name and match with the pictures.

ASLIOABT

INWMDLLI

IEKT

_____

_____

_____

UNIVERSE

Find the correct word from the box and fill in the blanks.

East   Shape   Stars   West

The sun rises in the _____ every morning.

The moon changes its _____ everyday.

There are a large number of _____ in the sky.

The sun sets in the _____ every evening.

Who am I?

I give you heat and light in the day time.

_____

We are many in number. We cover the sky at night.

_____

I come at night and change my shape everyday.

_____

I bring rain for you.

_____

Count the number of triangles in the given star.

_____

MIXED BAG

Colour the box green for the true statement.

Living things cannot breathe.

Non-living things can not eat.

A pen is a living thing.

We take rest in the bedroom.

We should not play with switches and plugs.

We can take our hands out of a moving vehicle.

A gentle wind is called storm.

River is a source of water.

We see a rainbow in the sky after a shower of rain.

The Sun changes its shape everyday.

We like to have tea in the hot weather.

Stem holds the plant upright.

Gram is a measuring unit.

Turtle is a non-living thing.

 ANIMALS

Look at the pictures carefully and write their names in the correct box.

Land animal

Amphibians

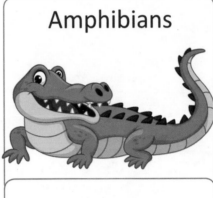

Water animal

Arboreal

Herbivorous

Reptile

Carnivorous

Scavenger

136

HOMES OF ANIMALS

Match the animals with their homes.

BODY PARTS

Christie is doing a few activities. Tick (✓) the correct organ that she will use in doing the activity.

Christie reads a book.

Christie eats her dinner.

 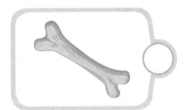 

Christie smells a flower.

Christie licks an ice cream.

Christie listens the music.

 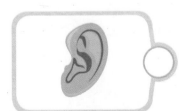 

THINKING SKILLS

 **ODD ONE OUT**

Tick (✓) the odd one out in each of the following sequence.

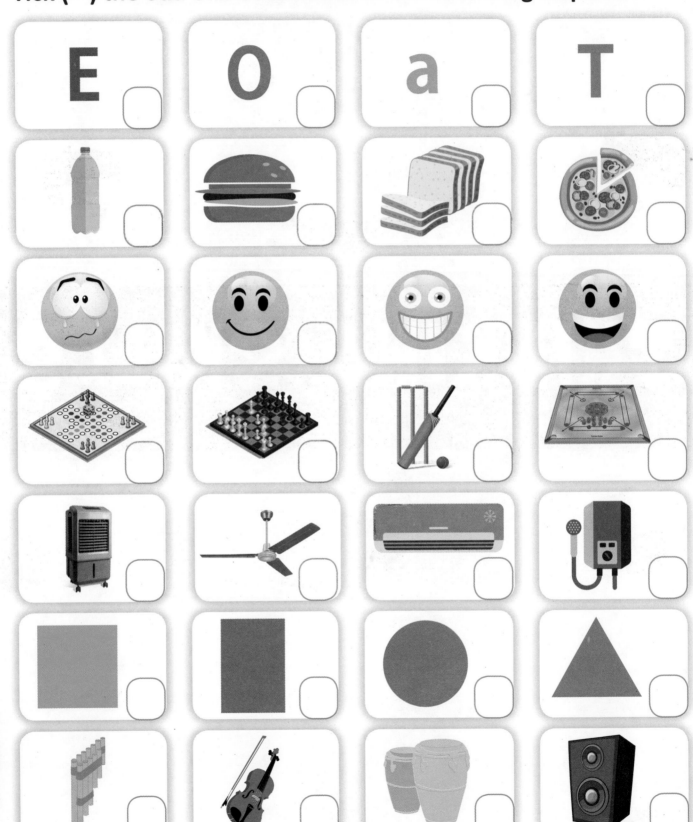

Tick (✓) the odd one out in each of the following sequence.

Tick (✓) the odd one out in each of the following sequence.

ANALOGY

Identify the relation between the given pair and find out the missing thing from the following sequence.

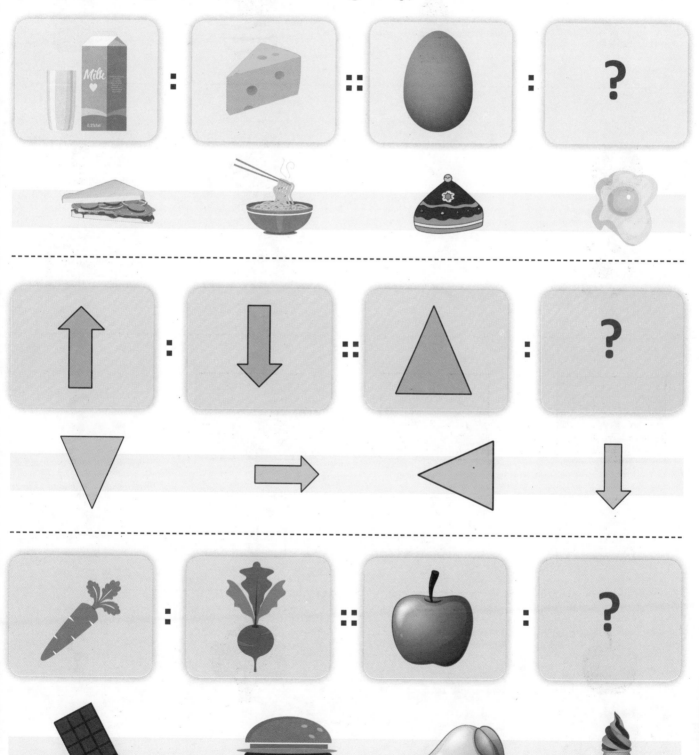

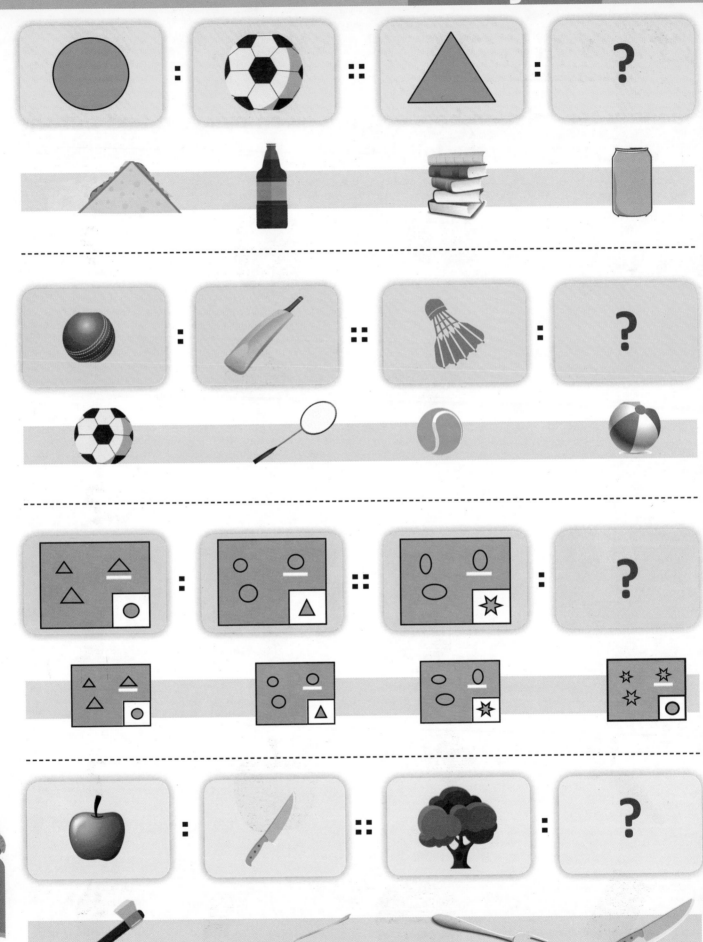

 :  ::  :

 :  ::  :

 :  ::  :

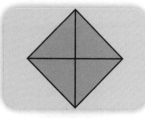 : 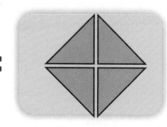 :: 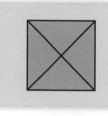 :

 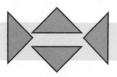 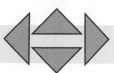

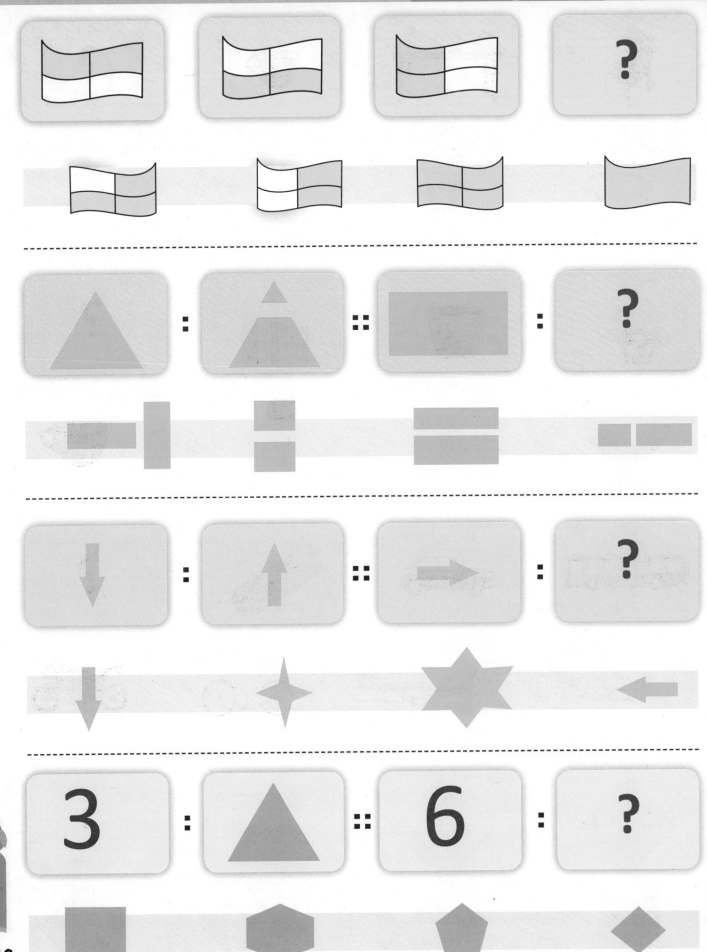

 :  ::  :

 :  ::  :

 :  ::  :

 :  ::  :

 :  ::  :

 :  ::  :

 :  ::  :

 :  ::  :

PATTERNS

Choose the correct option in each of the following questions.

Which number is missing in the following number pattern?

| 10 | 20 | 30 | ? | 50 | 60 |

| 20 | 40 | 50 | 60 |

Which is the missing letter in the following letter pattern?

| 31 | 32 | ? | 34 | 35 | 36 |

| 27 | 23 | 37 | 33 |

Which number is missing in the following number pattern?

| 17 | 16 | 15 | 14 | 13 | ? |

| 11 | 12 | 17 | 10 |

Which number is missing in the following number pattern?

| 30 | 25 | 20 | 15 | ? | 5 |

| 5 | 10 | 9 | 12 |

149

Tick (✓) the correct pattern.

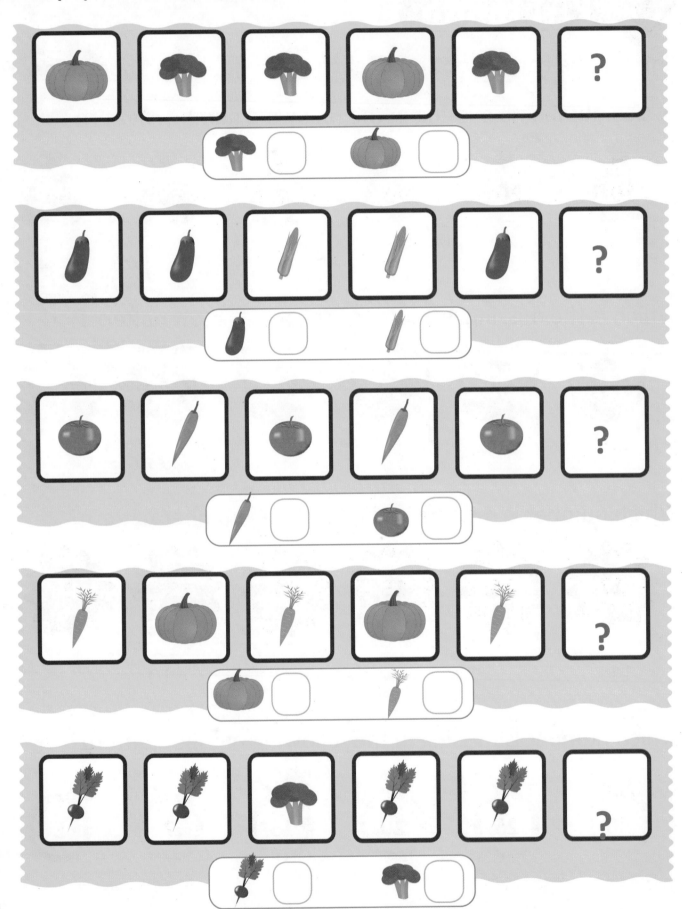

LIFE SKILLS

GOOD MANNERS

Good manners make good children.
Talking politely and listening to others are good manners.

Let us read the poem on good manners.

We say "Thank You"

We say "Please"

And "Excuse Me"

When we sneeze.

That is the way

We do what is right

We have manners

We are polite.

Tick (✓) the correct option.

We should say 'thank you' when we sneeze.

We should say 'please' when we sneeze.

We should say 'excuse me' when we sneeze.

Complete the words.

Never talk | b | | d | about others.

Never pick your | n | | s | e | in front of others.

Knock on the | d | | o | r | before entering a room.

When you call up someone on the phone,

first tell them who | y | | u | are.

Don't make | f | | n | of others.

Tick (✓) the good manners and cross (x) the bad manners.

Tick (✓) the good manners and cross (x) the bad manners.

GOOD HABITS

Fill in the blanks to complete the good habits chart.

MY GOOD HABITS CHART

I brush my _____ twice daily.

I _____ my hair morning and evening.

I clip my _____ every weekend.

I always sneeze into a _____.

I _____ my hands before and after a meal.

Clues: nails, teeth, comb, handkerchief, wash

Tick (✓) the images that show clean habits and cross (x) out the ones that don't.

RIGHT VS WRONG

Tick (✓) the correct ones and cross (x) the wrong ones.

DAILY ROUTINE

Look at the pictures given below. Write the number in the box indicating the correct order of these activities.

Fill in the blanks with the right word.

straight   clean   combed   hanky

dustbin   early

Wake up _____ in the morning.

Use your _____ while sneezing or coughing.

Use _____ to throw the waste.

Keep your hair _____ daily.

Wear _____ clothes everyday.

Always sit, walk and stand _____ .

HEALTHY HABITS

Tick (✓) the healthy foods and cross (x) the unhealthy food.

Colour the food that are healthy.

Complete the crossword puzzle.

1. _____ healthy, be healthy.

2. Chicken and eggs give us _____.

3. An _____ a day keeps doctor away.

4. _____ is called a complete food.

5. Bananas and oranges are _____.

A	P	P	L	E	P
Z	Y	Z	M	A	Y
F	R	U	I	T	S
Z	M	P	L	Q	L
L	Y	R	K	U	W
E	N	E	R	G	Y

State T for True and F for False.

Juice is better than soft drinks.

Chips are good for health.

We need milk for strong bones.

Burger, noodles and chocolates make teeth strong.

Fast food is a junk food.

CLEANLINESS

Tick (✓) against the things a good student should do and cross (x) the others.

- ○ Wash your face and brush your teeth every morning.
- ○ Wear dirty clothes.
- ○ Sleep without changing uniform
- ○ Eat meals without washing your hands.
- ○ Cut your nails regularly.
- ○ Throw bits of paper on the floor.
- ○ Do nail biting.
- ○ Cover your face when you sneeze. Say "Excuse me."
- ○ Comb your hair once in a week.
- ○ Make drawings on tables.

Tick (✓) the correct option.

Tia bought grapes at the market. She should immediately

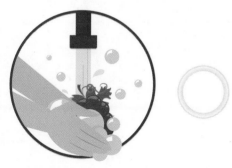

Rohan is hungry. He should opt for

A good hygiene for kids includes keeping his/her hands clean at all times.

Tick (✓) against the things a good student should do and cross(x) the others.

Sneeze or cough without covering mouth.

Wear clean uniform.

Throw bits of paper on the floor.

Share your towel.

Do your work hanky.

Spitting on floor.

Use clean tissues.

Wash hands before and after meals

What do you need to clean the following? Match them.

A	B
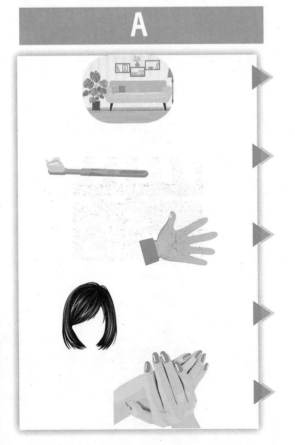	

teeth

shampoo

Broom

nail cutter

soap

Tick (✓) the correct picture.

Who keeps your school clean?

Where do you throw garbage?

 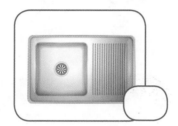 

What do you use to clean your teeth?

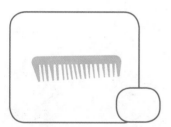 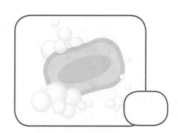 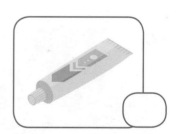

What do you do before going to sleep?

What is more important for you?

SAFETY

Which of the following activity is not safe? Tick (✓) them.

FUN WITH COLOURS

Colours

Read the colour words on the stars and colour them.

Orange Green Blue Purple

Yellow Pink Brown Red

Write the colour names below each colour.

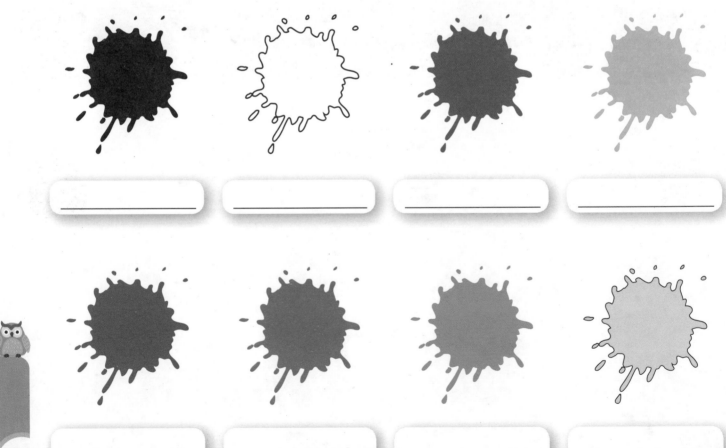

Colouring Fun

Colour the baby duck.

Colouring Fun

Colour the kites of your choice.

Matching Fun

Fill the colours in the stars with the colours of the matching objects.

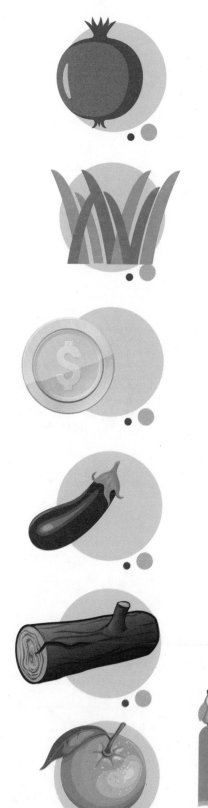

169

Number Joining

Join the Number dots and colour it.

Grid Drawing

Trace and colour the starfish in the grid.

Find Me

Circle the purple dino.

Tracing Fun

Parrots can speak some words that we speak! Trace and colour the parrot as indicated.

Symmetry

Trace and colour the cat as shown.

Fun with Colours

Code Colouring

Colour the Chameleon with colours indicated by numbers.

Number Joining

Join the number to complete the tomato. Colour it as shown.

Fun with Colours

Code Colouring

Sunflower seeds are used to make cooking oil. Colour the sunflower with colours indicated by numbers.

Tracing Fun

We keep books and notebooks in our school bag. Trace and colour the school bag as you like.

Code Colouring

Colour the picture as shown.

Colouring Pattern

Complete the colouring pattern given below.

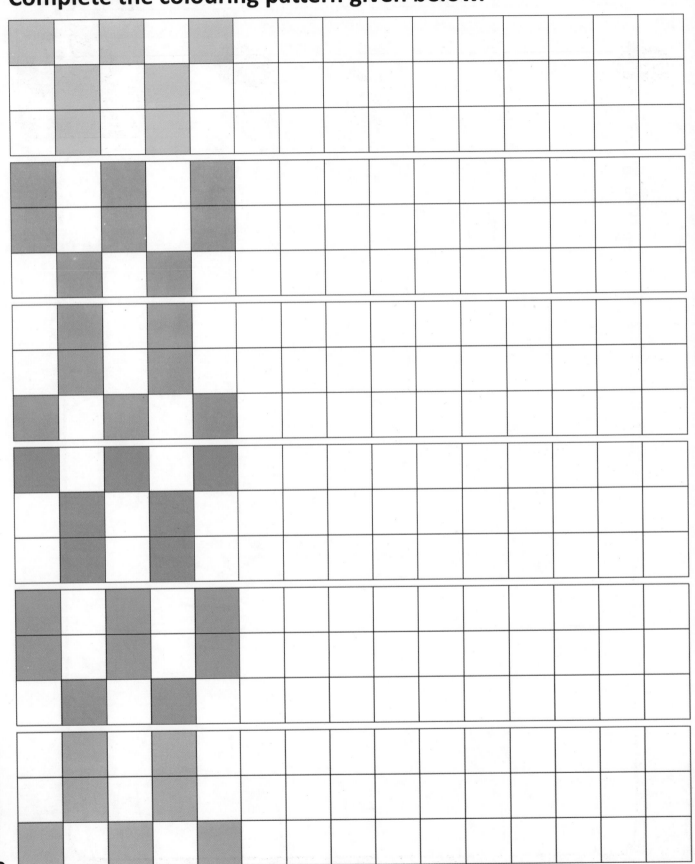

ACTIVITIES

Maze Game

Help the pirate reach the treasure island.

Find the Difference

Spot **5** differences in the given set of pictures.

Word Search

Find the words in the word search puzzle with the help of picture clues.

Ant

Ape

W	X	A	N	T	C	M	X
O	F	P	X	H	W	U	V
L	R	E	T	H	J	E	P
C	I	P	H	L	I	A	O
B	A	B	Y	O	O	X	I
A	R	O	S	N	A	C	Y
G	M	Z	U	I	J	B	E
E	T	K	L	N	D	W	R

Arm

Baby

184

Alphabet Matching

Circle the matching lowercase letter in each row.

R	a n o r e c w
S	m v c x a n s
T	u t r e J y f
U	e a o u r w m
V	w r n x c v u
W	v y w u d r e
X	x m v c a n o
Y	t c a y u f w
Z	e s n w r z c

Maze Game

Help the silly tomatoes find the rainbow.

Find the Difference

Spot **5** differences in the given set of pictures.

Maze Game

Help dino mamas find their eggs.

Find Me

Find and circle the dinosaur toys.

Word Search

Find the words in the word search puzzle with the help of picture clues. Colour them.

Bee

Fish

Bell

B	E	E	F	S	E	A	S
E	Z	J	A	T	D	A	U
L	A	N	D	D	U	C	K
L	Z	A	J	S	N	Z	M
S	P	G	F	L	T	Y	A
B	I	N	I	J	A	A	O
T	N	A	S	S	D	R	J
P	N	S	H	A	T	N	A

Bin

Yarn

Duck

CERTIFICATE
of ACHIEVEMENT
Presented to

FOR

DATE

SIGNED